Exploring Science:
Student Pages

Written by Paige Hudson

Exploring Science

Exploring Science

Copyright

All contents copyright ©2011 by Paige Hudson. All rights reserved.

Exploring Science

Unit 1:
Exploring the World Around Me

Exploring Science

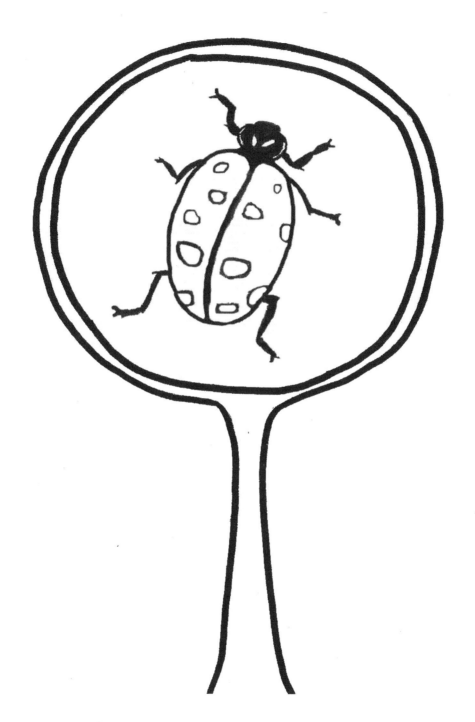

Observation is taking the time to look
at the world around you.

"Science Safari"

I saw the following things on my Science Safari...

_____

_____

_____

_____

_____

_____

_____

_____

_____

My Room

Student Pages 9

A natural community is a group of animals and plants that live in the same place.

"Circle of Earth"

I saw the following plants and animals in my circle of earth...

_____

_____

_____

_____

_____

_____

_____

_____

_____

My Community Collage

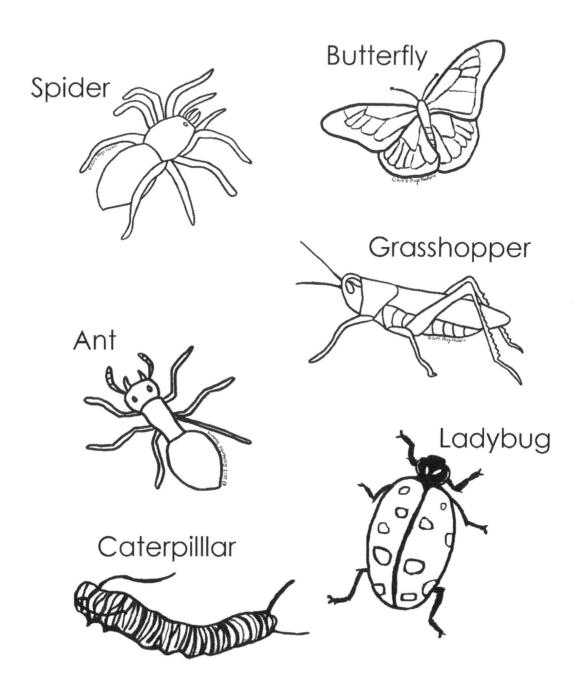

Spider

Butterfly

Grasshopper

Ant

Ladybug

Caterpilllar

Insects are my tiniest neighbors.

Exploring Science

"Bug Hotel"

The following bugs visited my hotel...

Sketch or picture of bug

____ legs

____ wings

____ body parts

____ eyes

____ legs

____ wings

____ body parts

____ eyes

Sketch or picture of bug

Sketch or picture of bug

____ legs

____ wings

____ body parts

____ eyes

"Bug Hotel"

The following bugs visited my hotel...

```
┌─────────────────────────────────┐
│      Sketch or picture of bug    │
│                                  │
│                                  │
│                                  │
│                                  │
│                                  │
│                                  │
└─────────────────────────────────┘
```

_____ legs

_____ wings

_____ body parts

_____ eyes

_____ legs

_____ wings

_____ body parts

_____ eyes

```
┌─────────────────────────────────┐
│      Sketch or picture of bug    │
│                                  │
│                                  │
│                                  │
│                                  │
│                                  │
│                                  │
└─────────────────────────────────┘
```

```
┌─────────────────────────────────┐
│      Sketch or picture of bug    │
│                                  │
│                                  │
│                                  │
│                                  │
│                                  │
│                                  │
└─────────────────────────────────┘
```

_____ legs

_____ wings

_____ body parts

_____ eyes

Insect Fingerprints

Student Pages 16

My backyard is full of interesting plants and animals.

Exploring Science

Picture of my Natural Museum

What I like best about my museum is...

_____

_____

_____

_____

_____

Painting with Nature

Exploring Science

Unit 2:
Exploring Water

Exploring Science

Water can change shape.

"Changing Shapes"

I saw water make the following shapes…

Blot It

Liquid water can move, but solid water keeps its shape.

"Wonderful Water"

My liquid water...

feels like...	
smells like...	
moves like...	
sounds like...	

My solid water...

feels like...	
smells like...	
moves like...	
sounds like...	

My Wiggly Water Necklace

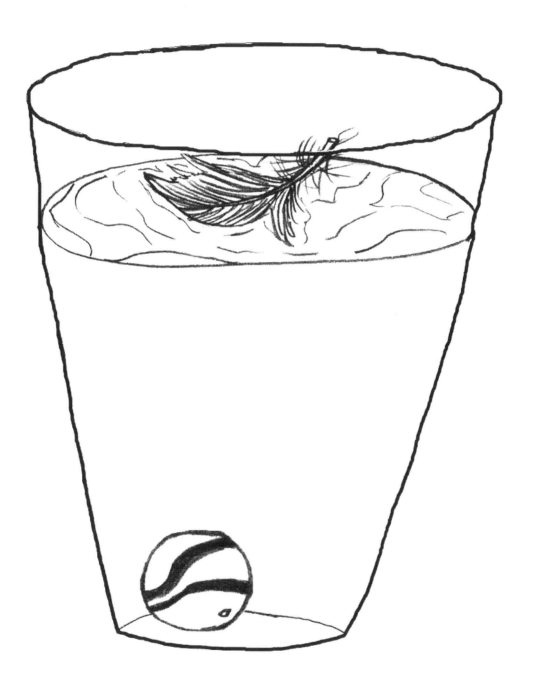

Some objects float in water;
some objects sink.

Exploring Science

"Floaters and Sinkers"

Object	Floats	Sinks

Crayon and Paint

Student Pages 31

Some materials soak up water (absorb),
while others keep it away (repel).

"Get Soaked"

Object	Absorbs	Repels

Fuzz Out

Unit 3:
Exploring Air

Exploring Science

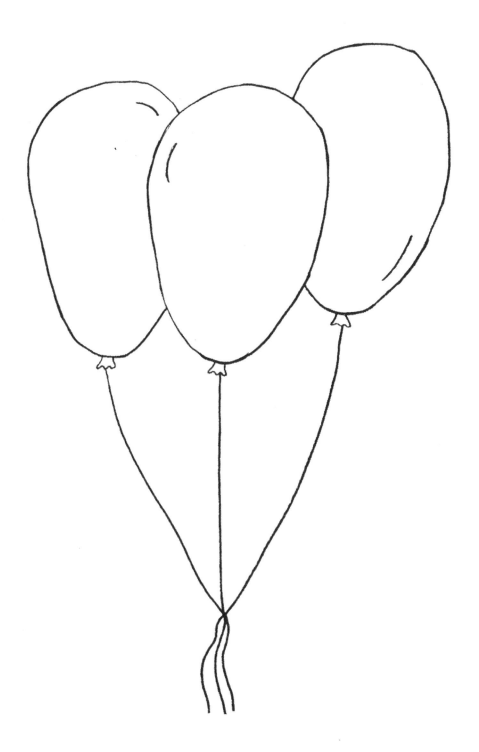

Air is everywhere!

"Is there air in there?"

I learned that air is...

_____

_____

_____

_____

_____

_____

_____

_____

_____

Shapes Kite

Student Pages 39

Wind blows and can move things.

"I'll Huff and Puff"

When I blew air into my hand, it felt...

_____

_____

_____

_____

_____

_____

_____

_____

_____ won our water race.

Air Painting

Student Pages 42

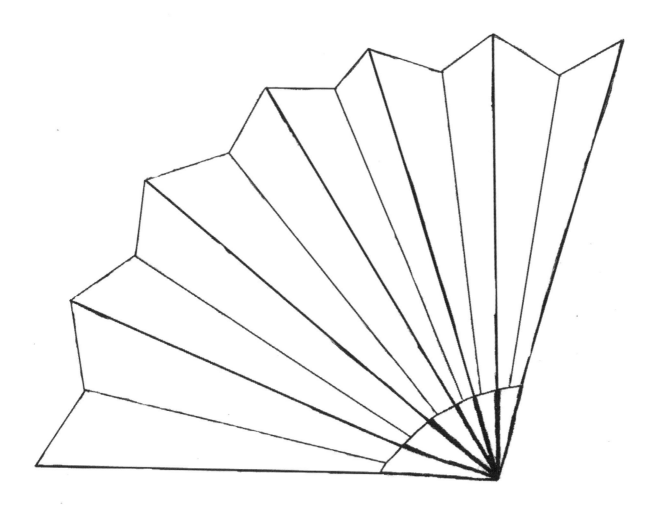

We can use fans to move air.

"Fan and Roll"

I learned that moving air can...

_____

_____

_____

_____

_____

_____

_____

_____

_____

_____

Fancy Fan

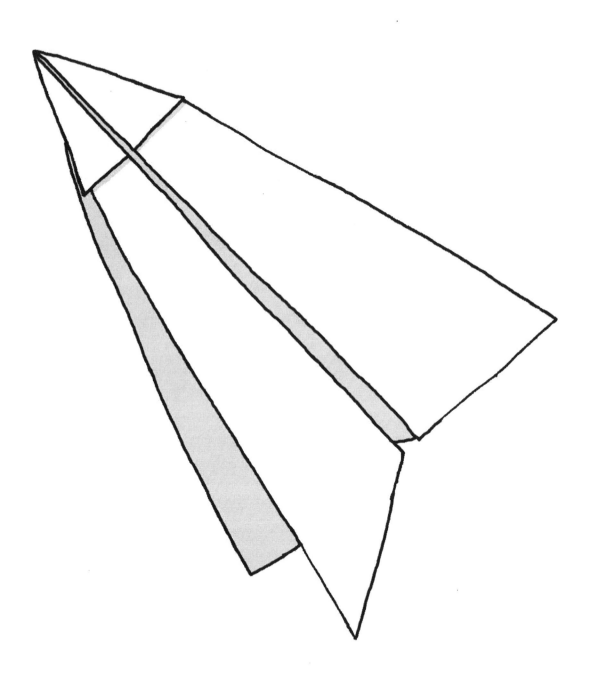

Moving air has a force than can lift objects.

"Air Spinners"

My three paper spinners looked like this...

I circled the one that "flew" the best.

Feathery Flight

Unit 4:
Exploring Weather

Exploring Science

A shadow is created when an object blocks out the Sun's light.

"Sunny Day, Shadow Play"

Time of Day	Length & Location of my shadow

Silhouette Collage

Rain is water falling from clouds in the sky.

"Raindrop Landing Pad"

Pitter Patter Paint

Clouds are made from water vapor.

Exploring Science

"Cloud in a Bag"

Picture of my bag

What I learned about clouds and rain...

_____

_____

_____

_____

Fluffy Clouds

Weather changes with the season.

"Weather Watch"

My weather this week...

Day	Weather
Monday	
Tuesday	
Wednesday	
Thursday	
Friday	

Seasons Collage

Weather Watch Stickers

Windy	Sunny	Cloudy	Stormy
Windy	Sunny	Cloudy	Stormy
Windy	Sunny	Cloudy	Stormy
Windy	Sunny	Cloudy	Stormy
Windy	Sunny	Cloudy	Stormy

Exploring Science

Unit 5:
Exploring Plants

Exploring Science

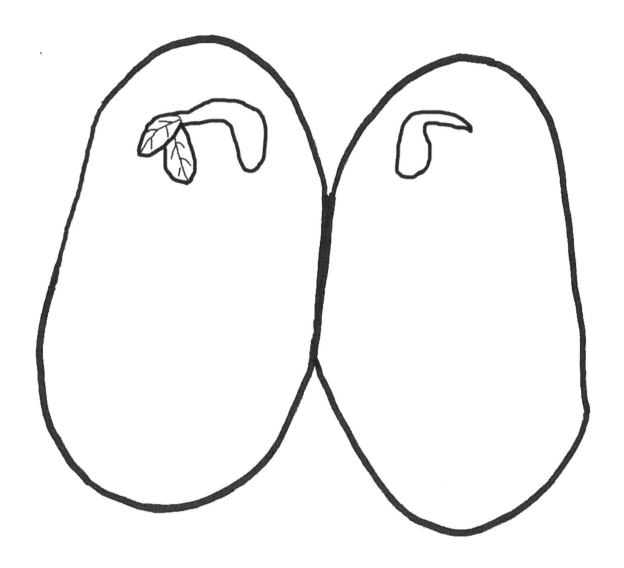

A seed contains a tiny baby plant.

"Pebble Plant"

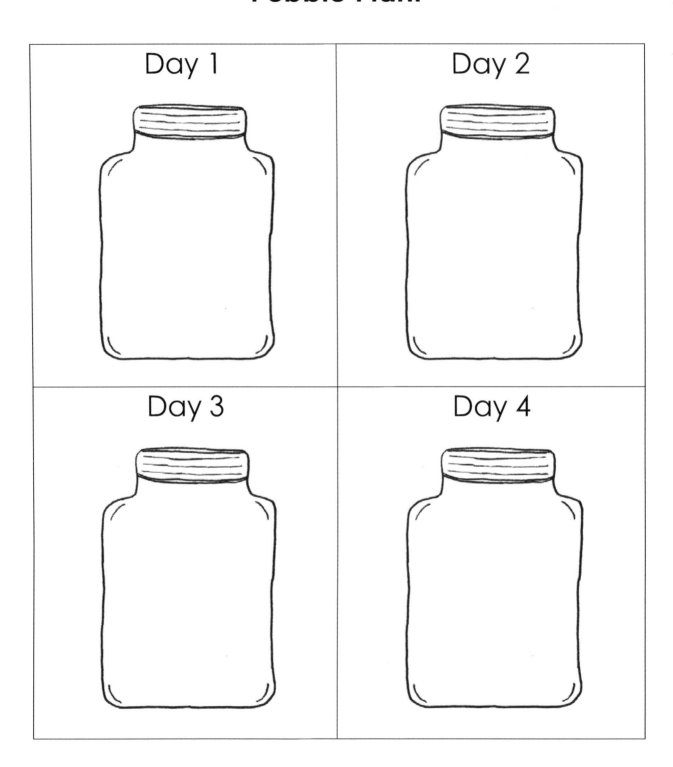

Day 1

Day 2

Day 3

Day 4

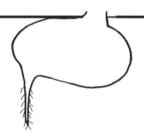

Bean Dream

All trees have a crown, trunk and roots.

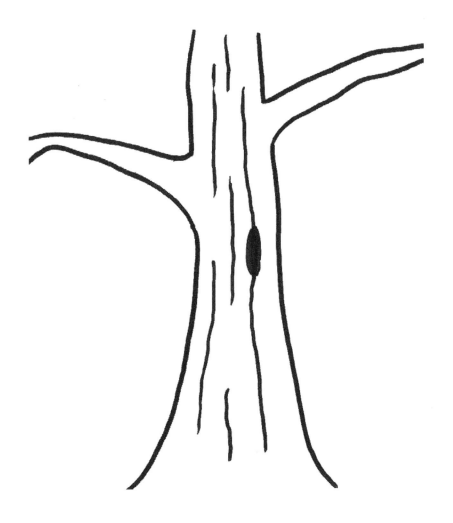

My Tree

Pine Tree Leaves

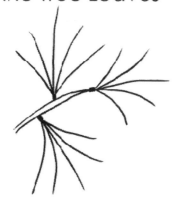

Maple Tree Leaf

Cherry Tree Leaf

Fern Leaf

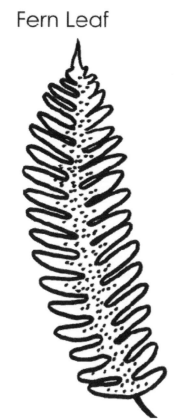

Flowering Plant Leaf

Leaves come in many shapes, sizes and shades of green.

Exploring Science

"Leaf Celebration"

I pressed the following leaves...

Leaf Prints

Flowers attract insects with a variety of colors and smells.

"Flower Power"

Picture of my fabric

What I learned about flowers...

_____

_____

_____

_____

Shapes Flower

Exploring Science

Unit 6:
Exploring the Earth

Exploring Science

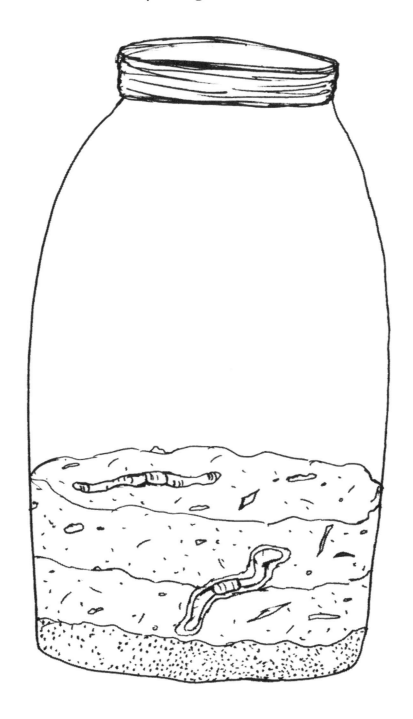

Dirt is made up of bits of rocks, dead plants
and dead animals.

"Inside Dirt"

I saw the following inside my dirt jar....

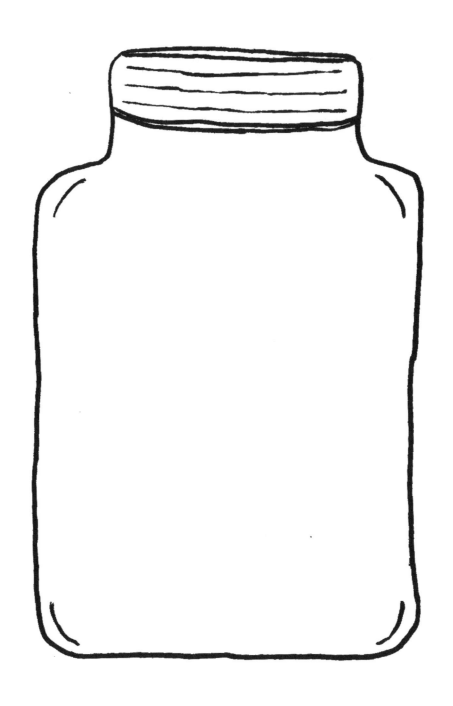

Painting with Dirt

Sand is finely ground rock.

"Earth Pies"

Picture of my Earth Pies

I learned that...

_____

_____

_____

_____

Painting with Sand

People use dirt, sand and clay to make bricks for their houses.

Exploring Science

"Brickworks"

Picture of my brick

I learned that...

_____

_____

_____

_____

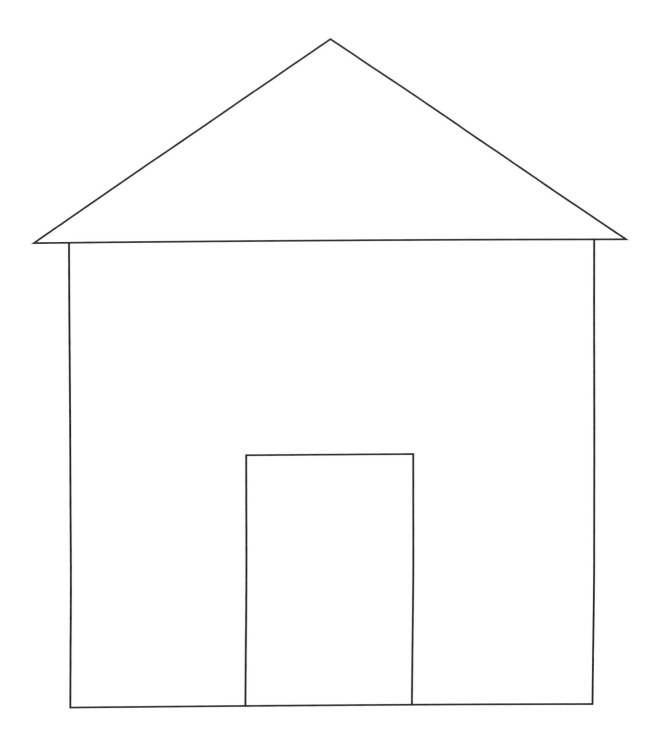

Sponge Brick House

Sedimentary
Rock

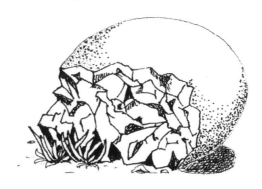

Metamorphic
Rock

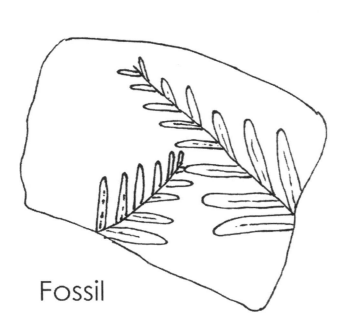

Fossil

Rocks come in different shapes and sizes.

"Rock Out"

Here are some of the rocks I collected...

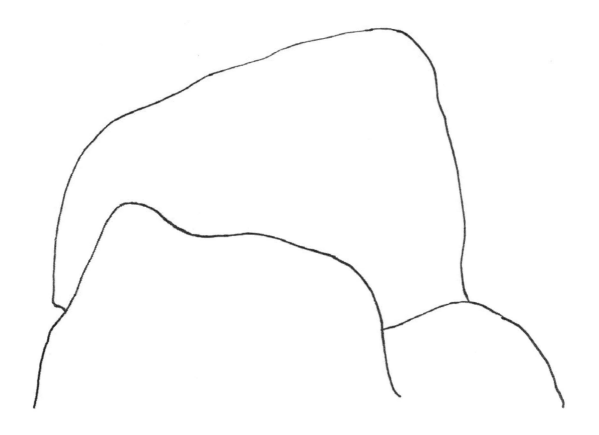

My Rocks

Unit 7:
Exploring Chemistry

Exploring Science

A solution is an even mixture of two
or more liquids.

"Purple Cow"

Milk   Grape Juice

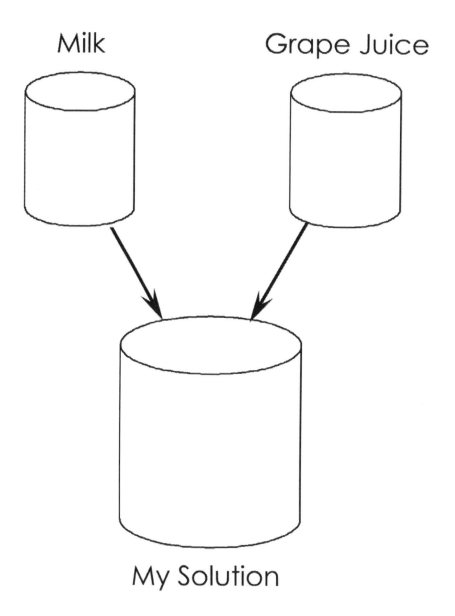

My Solution

I learned that...

_____

_____

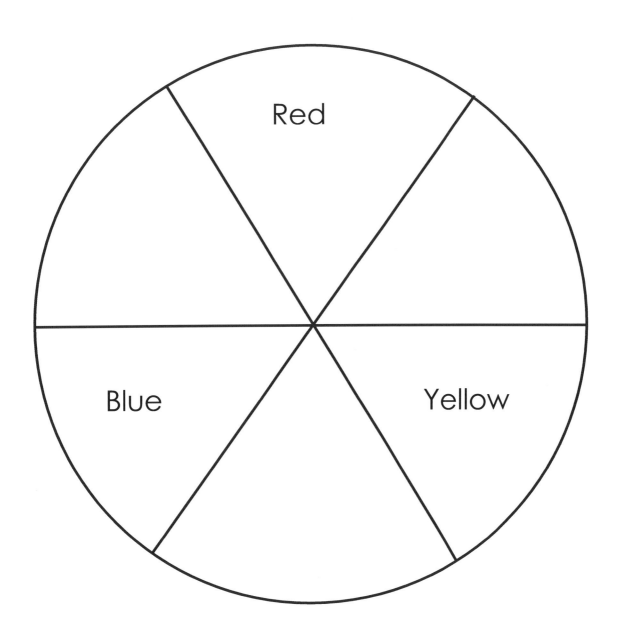

Color Wheel

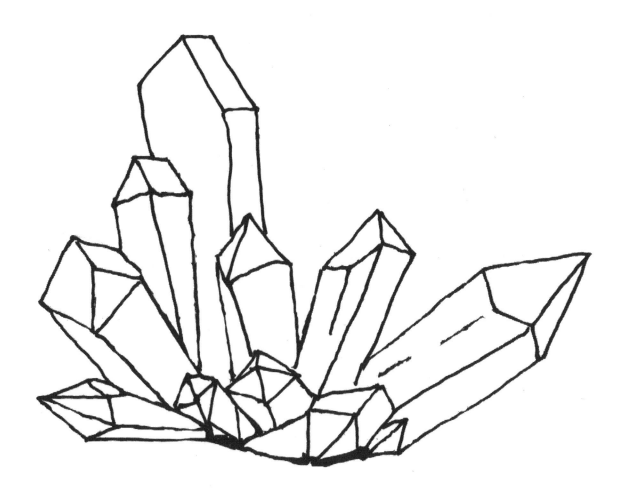

Crystals are solids with geometric shapes.

Exploring Science

"Sparkling Star"

Picture of my star

What I learned about crystals...

_____

_____

_____

_____

Sparkling Sheet

Heat from the Sun's rays can change food and water.

"Cooking with the Sun"

Picture of my oven

What I learned about heat...

_____

_____

_____

_____

Tissue Paper Sun

When a liquid gets really cold, it can freeze.

Exploring Science

"Ice Cream in a Bag"

I was able to make ice cream in a bag.

Yes   No

What I learned about freezing liquids…

_____

_____

_____

_____

_____

_____

_____

Painting with Ice

Unit 8:
Exploring Sound

Exploring Science

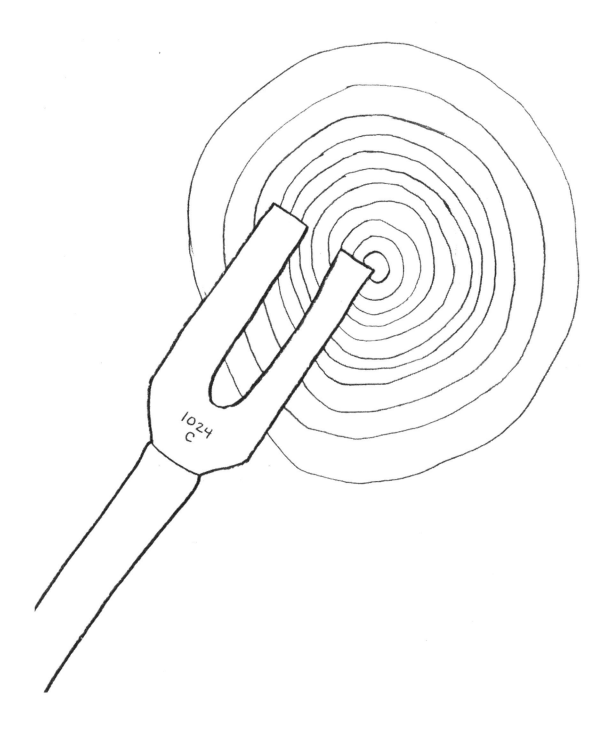

Sound waves are vibrations that can travel through the air.

Exploring Science

"See Sound"

I saw the following things today...

_____

_____

_____

_____

_____

_____

_____

_____

_____

_____

_____

Hum Gizmo

The larger an animal's ears,
the better it can hear.

"Trumpet Ears"

I was able to hear (better   /   worse   )

with my trumpet ears.

Today I learned that...

_____

_____

_____

_____

_____

_____

_____

_____

Screech Gizmo

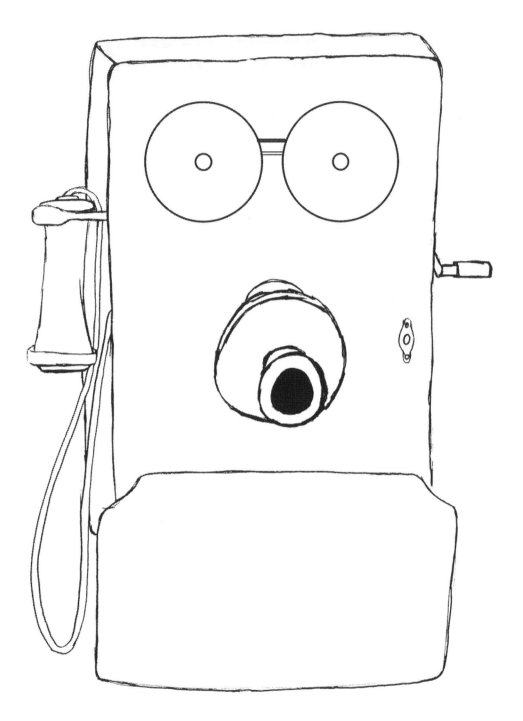

Sound waves can travel through the air,
through walls, and through string or wire.

"Party Line"

I (was   /   was not   ) able to hear the

messages from my party line.

Today I learned that...

_____

_____

_____

_____

_____

_____

_____

_____

Warble Gizmo

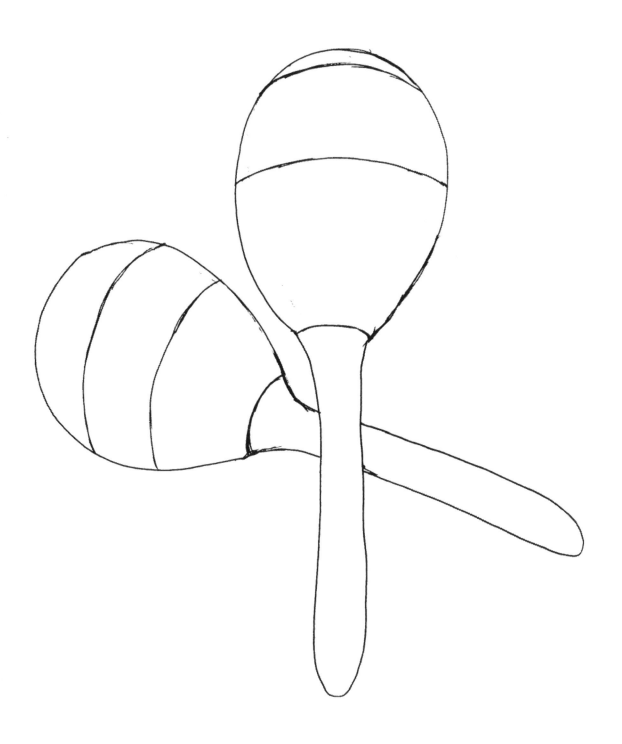

Different objects make different sounds.

"Shake and Rattle Game"

Draw a line to the matching containers...

#1   #6

#2   #7

#3   #8

#4   #9

#5   #10

Plate Shaker

Unit 9:
Exploring Motion

Exploring Science

Moving from one place to another
is called motion.

"Roller Derby"

I tested the following objects...

The _____ rolled the farthest.

Painting with Marbles

Student Pages 125

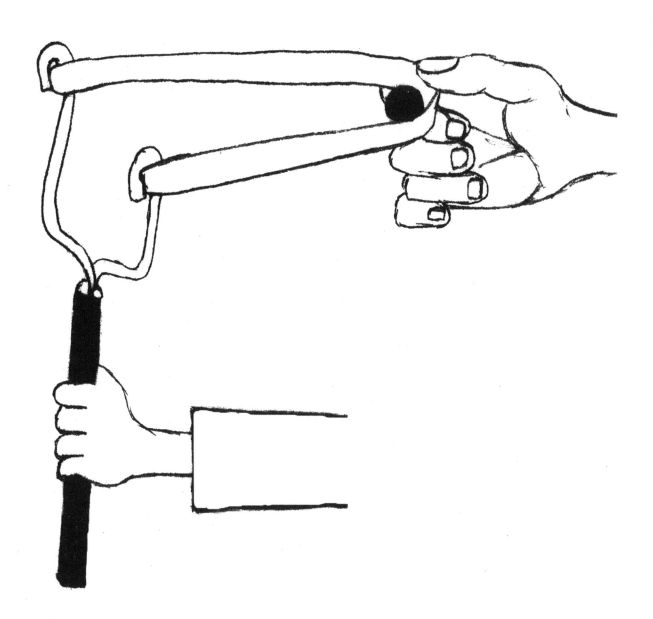

When stored energy is let out,
it causes motion.

"Flipping Elf"

Picture of my elf

What I learned about motion...

_____

_____

_____

_____

Painting with Energy

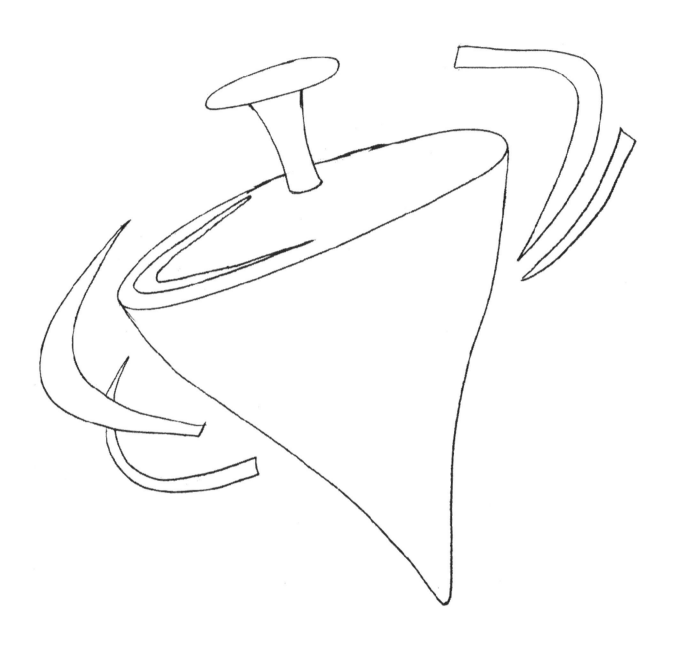

Spinning is a rapid turning or
whirling motion.

Exploring Science

"Super Spinners"

Picture of my spinners

What I learned about spinning...

_____

_____

_____

_____

Top Tracks

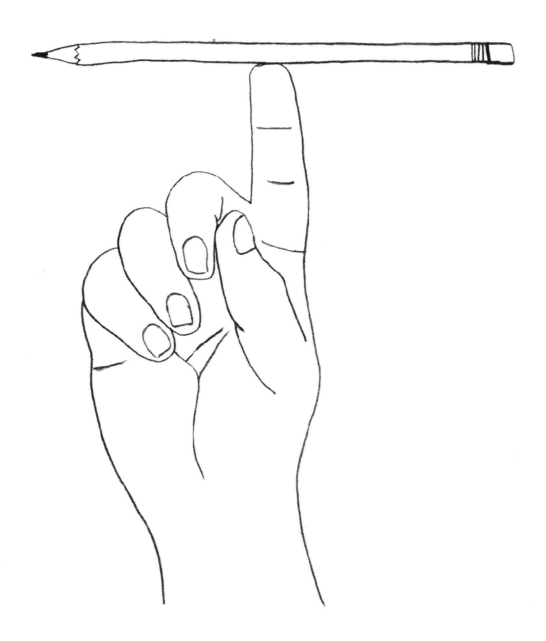

An object is in balance when the same weight is on either side.

"Balancing in Action"

Balancing on one foot is...

hard   easy

What I learned about balance...

_____

_____

_____

_____

_____

_____

_____

_____

Balancing in Art

Exploring Science

Exploring Science

25678809R00078

Made in the USA
Charleston, SC
12 January 2014